GREAT DEFENCES OF OUR TIME

by T.A.K.

THE HOWGATE PUBLISHING COMPANY, PENICUIK, SCOTLAND

FOREWORD

I've often pondered on the identity of TAK. It's the only secret Parliament House has ever kept. Even the identity of the author of Waverly was whispered about, long before the blame was pinned on that bankrupt old Tory Sheriff Scott. Perhaps it's all for the best. It means that we can honour our own satirist, whoever he may be, without any danger of him being given a Knighthood.

Here in this collection of cartoons is the beginning of wisdom. TAK shows the sharp wit that laughs not at others but at ourselves. He maps the country we have all walked across. He digs the holes we have fallen into. Look into these pits ye public and laugh at us, as we laugh at ourselves. These cartoons are the work of the keenest observer of all the mistakes that an advocate can ever make. I know, I've made them all myself.

Ian R. Hamilton Q. C.
Advocate and Author

INTRODUCTION

For over fifteen years TAK's work has been familiar to a select legal band. It later became more widely known to readers of "The Glasgow Herald" (now The Herald) and readers of a specialist medical publication. Two small booklets were once published.

Some of his cartoons were used in a book published in aid of an appeal for the Great Ormond Street Hospital for Sick Children and Yehudi Menuhin's 'Live Music Now' but this is the first time that they have been exposed to a wider audience.

Spanning as they do a period of fifteen years and representing only those cartoons which do not disclose identifiable situations they are a glimpse into some of the humour of the Bar. Those from the early days can be easily distinguished from later years when TAK was more able to indulge his obsessions for shooting and fishing.

Despite the exposure TAK has always remained anonymous and his face is known to few . . . as is demonstrated in the first cartoon.

The world of law has often appeared to be somewhat starchy and humourless : If this book does no more than expose that myth its purpose is achieved !

T.A.K.

" T.A.K. "

"...And it doesn't even work..."

" . . . So I asked the witness . . . could
you demonstrate how he stabbed you . . . ? "

"... It's up to you ... but I wouldn't speak for too long ..."

" I warned you a five iron was too much . "

" Always does it . . . .
says he likes to know which way
the court is running before he
starts . . . "

" ... I've seen him address the ball for
three days ... "

"..I just said, isn't that your bank
manager on the 5th..?"

" . . . That reminds me - shouldn't you be
in the appeal court today . . . ? "

" Let's see you talk yourself
out of that one...!"

" . . . What makes you think I'm
reluctant to be here . . . "

"...I think he misses the time off..."

Vacation

" . . . I'm afraid we don't do social climbing . . . "

"...He's trying to be first to <u>talk</u> a balloon across the Atlantic..."

"...Part of the problem is that it's based on English law..."

"..Has anybody seen my wig..?"

" . . . That could be a record . . . the
      goodwill to all men lasted 20 minutes . . . "

" . . . Regardless of the weather, Mr. Smithers,
I do not find your form of dress
appropriate . . . "

" . . . And ten happy Christmases
to you too, sir . . . "

" To writing to you wishing you
a merry Christmas - five Guineas "

"...What I really enjoy about Christmas
is that you can forget work...
and get your fees up to date..."

" He's trying to get appointed
as standing counsel to the
Royal Company of Archers "

" . . . It's up to you but my
vote is for guilty . . . "

" . . . It's very worrying, doc . . .
I keep believing my clients . . . "

"...If asked to demonstrate...
...don't over-elaborate..."

"...I'd feel a lot
better if you
could prescribe
five grand..."

" ...These <u>can't</u> be my records ... I don't even know where Hypochondria is ..."

"... Either the set's on the blink again ... or he's a lawyer ... "

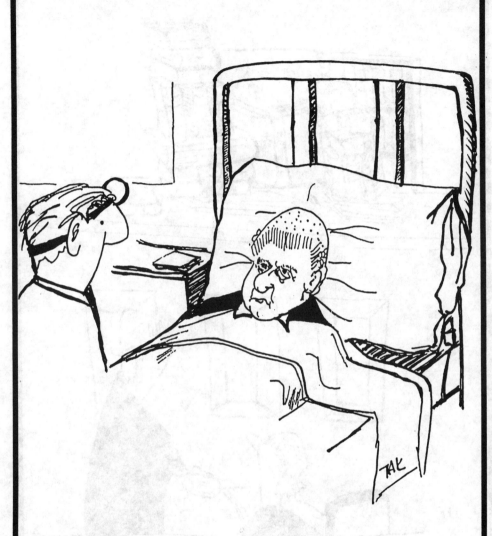

"You're going to
be fine . . . but we're
going to have to remove your
wig . . . "

"...Of course he's still there he never
leaves without his specs..."

"... I've just had a
parking ticket..."

" . . . I'm not saying he's lying . . .
he's mistaken me for
somebody else . . ."

" Are you able to continue now,
Dr. Jekyll ? . . . "

" . . . And what do you do for a
living, Mr. Coco . . . ? "

" . . . could you come back next week, . . . please . .
. . . I've run out of sentences . . . "

IN 1991 STRENUOUS EFFORTS
WERE BEING MADE TO IMPROVE
THE STANDARDS OF COMFORT
FOR WITNESSES WAITING TO BE
CALLED.

THE INCREASED PRESSURE ON
THE COURTS HAD
OVERSTRETCHED MANY OF THE
COURT FACILITIES AND WAITING
TIME FOR WITNESSES HAD
INCREASED SIGNIFICANTLY.

BROCHURES WERE NOW
PREPARED FOR THEM GIVING
THEM BETTER DIRECTIONS AND
ADVICE RELATING TO WHAT THEY
COULD EXPECT.

" . . . I didn't mean that you
should make yourself THAT
comfortable . . . sir . . . "

" . . . They're discussing
a plea, I think . . . "

" . . . In the first place . . . that is <u>not</u> the witness room . . . that is the dock

In the second place . . . <u>I</u> don't serve tea . . .
. . . and . . .
In the third place . . . please don't address me as 'Mrs' . . . "

" . . . Is this competent, Mr. Smithers ? . . "

" . . . I trust I'm not boring your Lordship . . . "

" I suggest we have <u>your</u>
   evidence in the Crown . . . <u>my</u>
   evidence in the Royal . . . <u>submissions</u>
   in the George and <u>verdict</u>
   in the Caledonian Club . . . "

"...I'm not saying he's broke but the perfume he gave his wife at Christmas was called *Extract of Decree*..."

" could you lend me a
fiver 'til Friday . . . ? "

" . . . How much is 1500 ECUs a day ? . . . "

" . . . Gold is up two points but paper
doesn't seem to be moving at all. "

" ... You'd think somebody would tell
them how odd they look ... "

"...So much for do it your self divorce..."

" . . . No, I'll take a budgie
. . . de minah birds *non curat lex* . . . "

IN 1994 A HEATED DEBATE
BEGAN IN SCOTLAND AS TO
WHETHER OR NOT THE
TELEVISION CAMERAS SHOULD
BE ALLOWED INTO THE COURTS.

TELEVISION WAS EVENTUALLY
ALLOWED IN ON AN
EXPERIMENTAL BASIS..............TAK
WAS OPPOSED TO THE
EXPERIMENT !

WHETHER THE RESULT WOULD
HAVE BEEN THE SAME HAD THE
"OJ SIMPSON" TRIAL BEEN
STARTED AT THE TIME MUST
REMAIN A MATTER OF
CONJECTURE !

"...So...if you think he's... <u>GUILTY</u>...
phone...0800...500...600....
...For <u>NOT</u> GUILTY ... Phone... 0800...
500...700..."

"...Wallington - Grunge, Advocate...
Specialist subject....
Carnal knowledge..."

"Could I just have that
submission again...
from the top...
...just for a sound check..."

" . . . By the way, your wife phoned . . .
seems you went out without your wig . . . "

" . . . Spends far too much time in
    Glasgow High Court, if you ask me . . . "

"... couldn't be my fingerprints
sir... they took them the
last time I was in..."

AWARDS OF DAMAGES IN THE
COURTS IN ENGLAND WERE...AND
REMAIN SIGNIFICANTLY HIGHER
THAN THOSE MADE IN
SCOTLAND.

THIS CARTOON ACCOMPANIED
AN ARTICLE ON COMPARISONS
OF AWARDS NORTH AND SOUTH
OF THE BORDER.

" ... The difference between Scots and
        English damages seems to be <u>nothing</u> ...
    ......you just add it on at the end..."

" . . . When it comes to the question
of damages, ladies and gentlemen,
you may find this helpful . . . "

"... I washed it last night and
I can't do a thing with it ..."

THIS CARTOON WHICH WAS
DRAWN IN 1985 WAS SOMEWHAT
AHEAD OF ITS TIME !

IN 1995 A PILOT STUDY WAS
UNDERTAKEN IN TWO AREAS OF
SCOTLAND TO INTRODUCE THE
TEACHING OF SOME ASPECTS
OF CRIMINAL LAW INTO SCHOOLS
AND TAK WAS INVOLVED IN THE
PROJECT.

Minister says law should be
taught in school.

" ... In my opinion, Mr. Fawkes,
... They will never prove it ... "

"... The pressure's beginning to tell -
poor chap never gets to sleep
before lunch..."

"... Very nice ...
... Pity he moved
in <u>before</u> he
retired ..."

"He claims it could be a real alternative to the jury system."

" The joys of country practice "

" . . . The green bits are grass, Sir . . . "

"...If he calls me learned comrade one more time I'll hit 'im..."

"..I can't say that I approve of your lordship's broad axe approach"

DAY 44.

"... You've forgotten what the charge is?
... I've forgotten who my
client is ..."

DURING THE 1980'S THERE
WERE A NUMBER OF TRIALS
INVOLVING MULTIPLE ACCUSED
ARISING OUT OF PRISON RIOTS.

OVERCROWDING IN THE PRISONS
WAS SAID BY SOME TO BE THE
ROOT CAUSE OF THE PROBLEMS.

THE CONDUCT OF THESE TRIALS
WITH SO MANY
ACCUSED,COUNSEL AND
SOLICITORS BEFORE THE BAR OF
THE COURT CREATED
SIGNIFICANT PROBLEMS FOR
THE MANAGEMENT OF THE
TRIAL.

"... My client claims its all about
overcrowding ..."

" . . What'll they think of next . . .
. . . womanless rapes . . . ? "

" . . . I think he dropped 50p down
the drain . . . "

"...It's called Appeal Court soup
- it sits all day without stirring..."

" The relationship between the brain
and the mouth establishes beyond
any doubt that this was an early
advocate ... "

DURING THE 1980'S QUESTIONS
AROSE AS TO HOW INTERNAL
DISCIPLINE IN THE FACULTY
SHOULD BE CONDUCTED.

FOR THE FIRST TIME IN ITS LONG
HISTORY IT WAS DECIDED THAT
A CODE OF CONDUCT SHOULD BE
PROMULGATED SETTING OUT
THOSE MATTERS WHICH HAD
FORMERLY BEEN HISTORICAL
CONVENTIONS.

THE CODE OF CONDUCT WHICH
FOLLOWS WAS **NOT** THE ONE
WHICH WAS ADOPTED !

CODE

OF

CONDUCT

RULE 1

An advocate is an officer of the court and will conduct himself with dignity and decorum at all times in court.

This rule forbids not only the obvious, thus . . . .

TAK

but also,....

any conduct likely to distract
the court or an opponent from
the business in hand.

This most important rule
is not, however

limited in its application to
the courtroom:

An advocate is an advocate
twenty four hours each day
and must never allow himself
to forget this.

RULE 2

Objections, when taken, should be accompanied by at least ordinary courtesy.

Cheating or sharp practice of any description is out of the question.

RULE 3

An advocate must accept instructions when properly tendered and accompanied by a reasonable fee.

There are of course exceptions to this rule - some of which will be obvious - some not so obvious.

RULE 4

An advocate may not advertise his services or otherwise tout for business.

There are of course, many
ways of advertising and
unless this rule is observed
in the spirit rather than the
letter....

.......strange results can ensue.

RULE 5

An advocate must never attempt to deceive the court, to mislead the court or deliberately withhold information from the court.

Failure to observe this
rule is seldom difficult
to spot.

RULE 6

An advocate should not identify himself personally with his clients position : this is inconsistent with

his position as an officer of the court.

PROSECUTION IN SCOTLAND IS CONDUCTED BY THE CROWN IN THE NAME OF THE LORD ADVOCATE.

UNDER HIGHLY EXCEPTIONAL CIRCUMSTANCES "PRIVATE" PROSECUTION MAY BE POSSIBLE.

IN 1982 THE FIRST MAJOR PRIVATE PROSECUTION OF THE CENTURY TOOK PLACE RESULTING IN LENGTHY DEBATE ON THE COMPETENCE OF THE PROSECUTION.

INEVITABLY THE DEBATE ATTRACTED ENORMOUS PUBLICITY AND INVOLVED THE EXPLORING OF THE LAW ON THE SUBJECT GOING BACK TO THE CASE OF THE INFAMOUS "BODYSNATCHERS" BURKE AND HARE .

"...as prosecutions go it doesn't
seem very private..."

SHORTLY AFTER RETURNING TO
BUSINESS AFTER THE NEW
YEAR A JUDGE........ BY A SLIP
OF THE TONGUE ....BACKDATED
A SENTENCE ON AN ACCUSED
TO "SEPTEMBER 1991"...INSTEAD
OF "SEPTEMBER 1992."

THE MATTER WAS SWIFTLY
REMEDIED BEFORE ANY HARM
WAS DONE !

" ...Sch ... it's usually
<u>February</u> before he finds
out he's been backdating
sentences to the previous year ... "

"... and finally m'lord ..."

PRODUCT RANGE

If you enjoyed reading this book then you may want to consider the range of products that are available through The Howgate Publishing Company. We cater for individuals or firms who may want to commission new cartoons or use existing ones for Christmas cards, calendars and general stationery. Prints signed by the author are also available. If you want more information write to the following address:

THE HOWGATE PUBLISHING COMPANY
P.O. BOX 13805
PENICUIK
MIDLOTHIAN
EH26 1YW

Below is a list of some of the products available:

PRINTS (FRAMED)

PRINTS (UNFRAMED)

CALENDAR: SPIRAL BOUND, PERSONALISED

CALENDAR: SINGLE A4 CARD, PERSONALISED

PERSONALISED XMAS CARDS

NON PERSONALISED XMAS CARDS